FOLENS
IDEAS BANK
VICTORIAN BRITAIN

Martin Frampton
John Edgar

Contents

Folens
Publishers

How to use this book

Ideas Bank books provide ready to use, practical, photocopiable activity pages for children, **plus** a wealth of ideas for extension and development.

TEACHER IDEAS PAGE **PHOTOCOPIABLE ACTIVITY PAGE**

Clear focus to the activity.

Background information and other help given.

Suggestions for extension writing.

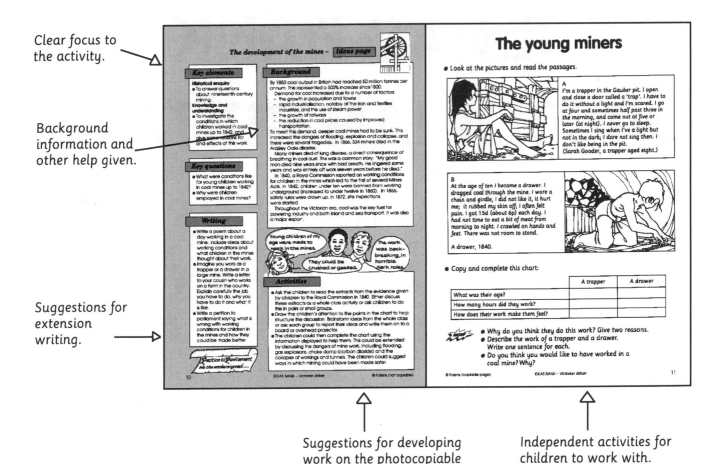

Suggestions for developing work on the photocopiable pages further.

Independent activities for children to work with.

● Time-saving, relevant and practical, **Ideas Bank** books ensure that you will always have work ready to hand.

Editors: Alyson Jones and Edward Rippeth   Layout artist: Suzanne Ward
Illustrations: Bob Farley (Graham-Cameron Illustrations)   Cover image: National Museum of Wales   Cover design: In Touch Creative Services
Photograph / print acknowledgements: Mansell Collection (9), Mary Evans Picture Library (21) and Hulton-Deutsch Collection Ltd (35).
The authors and publishers wish to thank Paul Allen for his design work on pages 19 and 44.
© 1997 Folens Limited, on behalf of the authors.

Every effort has been made to contact copyright holders of material used in this book. If any have been overlooked, we will be pleased to make any necessary arrangements. British Library Cataloguing in Publication Data. A catalogue record for this book is available from the British Library.
First published 1997 by Folens Limited, Dunstable and Dublin.
Folens Limited, Albert House, Apex Business Centre, Boscombe Road, Dunstable, LU5 4RL, England.
ISBN 1 85276907-6
Printed by Ashford Colour Press.

Introduction

The Victorian era is the period of British history from 1837 to 1901 named after the longest reigning British monarch. Queen Victoria ruled for nearly 64 years and was a unifying force during a period of great social, economic and political change.

The Industrial Revolution, which began at the end of the eighteenth century, accelerated during the Victorian Era. Industrial and commercial change, a world-wide Empire and a powerful navy all sought to promote the notion of British superiority. The Great Exhibition of 1851 demonstrated British power and prestige. This was a period of great advances in science and technology: suspension bridges, steam ships, power looms and new mining equipment. Significant medical discoveries improved surgical techniques, the development of anaesthetics encouraged more complicated operations. Old established attitudes were challenged: Darwinism forced a reappraisal of the origins of humanity.

Victorian Britain is characterised by the development of towns. Large industrial centres developed in the North and Midlands around Newcastle, Leeds, Liverpool, Manchester and Birmingham. For the first time, the majority of the British population became urban dwellers working in factories. Squalid living and working conditions were gradually improved with the assistance of Parliament and individual entrepreneurs, but considerable differences remained between the upper, middle and lower classes.

Victorian Britain was a rigid class society with different attitudes and behaviour. There were marked differences in lifestyles between the rich and the poor. While the wealthy went to public school, university and toured Europe, the masses worked long hours in damp and dangerous conditions for very little money. There was little government help for the sick or injured until the problem became acute. Improvements in living standards did occur as the pace of change accelerated throughout this period.

Legislation improved and regulated working conditions, removing some of the worst excesses of the factory system. A system of local government was established to improve town conditions and maintain public health. A series of inventions improved and transformed people's lives, including the gas light, the electric light, the sewing machine and the steam engine. The development of rail communications eroded regional differences, widened horizons and encouraged the movement of people.

Slow political reform extended the franchise to the middle and lower class, increasing the power of the House of Commons. While Europe suffered revolutions in 1848 and 1871, Britain remained calm and confident in its general policy of gradual change. The British Empire – a source of raw materials and markets – appeared supreme. Queen Victoria, as Head of the Empire, was the symbolic and unifying force commanding respect and loyalty. Her silver (1862), golden (1887) and diamond (1897) jubilees were the cause of huge national celebrations. Britain was at the height of its power and prestige: it controlled two-fifths of the world and was seen as an empire on which 'the sun never set'.

The ideas in this book offer teachers a rich variety of photocopiable resources that explore these themes. The activities address the full range of key elements through a range of lively classroom tasks. These include questioning the motives of some of the main personalities, evaluating primary source material and decision-making based on appropriate background information.

The Victorian era – Ideas page

Key elements

Chronology
● To place Victoria's children in the correct order from eldest to youngest.

Historical enquiry
● To answer questions about Victoria's family using the information on the activity page.

Key questions

● How many children did Queen Victoria have?
● Which European royal families were linked to the British monarch by marriage?

1840	Victoria m. Frederick
1841	Albert Edward m. Alexandra
1842	Alice m. Ludwig
1844	Alfred m. Marie
1846	Helena m. Christian
1848	Louise m. Marquise of Larne
1850	Arthur m. Louise
1853	Leopold m. Helena
1857	Beatrice m. Henry

Writing

● Imagine you are Victoria. Write a speech to describe your family.
● Using all of the information on the page, describe the influence Victoria had on the royal families of Europe.

Background

When Victoria became Queen in 1837, aged 18, the monarchy was unpopular – her predecessor William IV was known as 'Silly Billy'. Under the guidance of the two political giants of the century, William Gladstone and Benjamin Disraeli, Victoria became the focal point of a nation undergoing rapid social, economic and political change. She came to stand for values such as the family, patriotism, stability and social class.

During her reign Britain became known as the 'workshop of the world', exporting more than one third of the world's manufactured goods by 1870. The 1851 Great Exhibition, partly organised by Prince Albert and visited by Victoria, provided an opportunity for the British people to marvel at the wonders of this new technological and scientific age.

The huge wealth generated by these changes enabled Britain to develop a world-wide Empire. This required an expansion of military power and Britain became the undisputed 'super power'. In 1876 Disraeli made Victoria Empress of India.

Britain had a growing middle class and many people's standard of living improved. However, approximately one third of the population remained in abject poverty throughout the reign. The problem of poverty was not adequately addressed until the mid-twentieth century.

In 1887 and 1897 celebrations were held to celebrate the fiftieth and sixtieth years of Victoria's reign. These united British subjects of all classes and races from around the Empire.

Activities

● The children could construct a time line showing Victoria's children and their spouses.
● They could also use an atlas to investigate the countries from which the children's spouses came. They could draw their own map of Europe and write the names in the relevant places.
● Extension activities could include extending the family tree and the time line to investigate how today's royal family links to that of Victoria.
● More able children could investigate why Victoria had so many children and why they all married foreign princes and princesses.

IDEAS BANK – *Victorian Britain*

The Victorian era

Here is Queen Victoria's family tree. She was born in 1819.

Eldest child | | | **QUEEN VICTORIA = PRINCE ALBERT** | | | | Youngest child

=	=	=	=	=	=	=	=	=
Frederick (German)	Alexandra (Danish)	Ludwig (German)	Marie (Russian)	Christian (German)	Marquis of Larne (Irish)	Louise (German)	Helena (German)	Henry (German)

Key: = marriage

- Her children are listed below. Write them on the family tree in order from the eldest to the youngest.

Alice 1842	Arthur 1850	Alfred 1844
Helena 1846	Albert Edward 1841	Leopold 1853
Victoria 1840	Beatrice 1857	Louise 1848

- How many boys and how many girls did Victoria have?
- What is the age difference between the youngest and eldest?
- How old was Queen Victoria when her first and last children were born?
- Copy and complete this chart to showing where the husbands and wives came from.

Germany	Denmark	Russia	Ireland

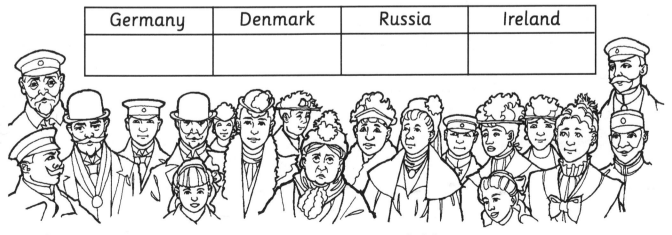

- Why did Victoria have so many children?
- Find out what happened to Prince Albert in 1861.
- What colour clothes did Victoria wear after this? Why?

Britain in the 1830s – Ideas page

Key elements

Knowledge and understanding

- To identify elements of change and continuity from pictures of a village at two different times.
- To give some reasons why changes occurred.
- To describe some of the changes in the village.

Key questions

- What changes can you see?
- What might have caused some of these changes?

CHANGES LATER IN THE VICTORIAN ERA

* Better trains carrying passengers.
* Steam-powered iron ships.
* Steam-powered tractors in the fields.
* More industry.
* Fewer people working in larger fields.

Writing

- Imagine you are writing a history book about Britain in the 1830s. Write two paragraphs to show your ideas about the reasons for some things changing while other things stayed the same.

Background

At the start of Queen Victoria's reign, Britain was a largely agricultural nation. Most people lived in the countryside and worked in farming. However, industrialisation had started.

Britain was the first country to industrialise for many reasons, including its natural resources (such as coal and iron) and having the Empire as a market and a supplier of raw materials.

To people at the time the changes that occurred between 1830 and 1900 were staggering. They were born into a world where much of day-to-day life had changed little since the 1500s. In particular, the technology of farming had remained virtually unaltered since the Middle Ages.

The effect that industrialisation had on society was enormous. Towns and cities grew, agriculture became less important as more and more people worked in the factories and more of the nation's wealth was created there. However, compared to this century, the pace of change was quite slow.

Activities

- As well as generally spotting the differences between the two pictures, the children could focus on specific elements of the pictures, picking out relevant information and identifying change and continuity.
- Discussion about possible causes should focus on the specific elements of the pictures in the context of the broader historical changes that took place during that period.
- Extension activities could include discussing what further changes might have occurred in the pictures later in the Victorian era.
- The children could also relate these pictures to changes they have experienced in their own locality, such as the construction of a new road or a housing estate.

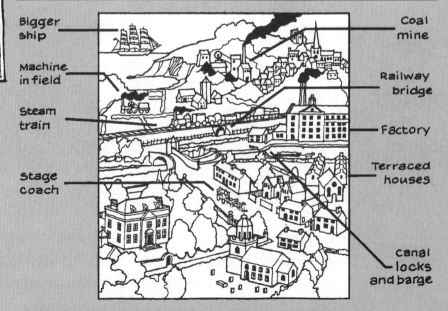

Bigger ship · Coal mine · Machine in field · Railway bridge · Steam train · Factory · Stage coach · Terraced houses · Canal locks and barge

Britain in the 1830s

- Look carefully at the two pictures below.

Britain in the 1750s   Britain in the 1830s

- Copy this chart. Using the pictures, write as much information as you can. One has been done for you.

	Britain in the 1750s	Britain in the 1830s
transport (roads and railways)	rough roads horses and carts no railway	better roads horses and carts railway boats on river
industry (factories)		
farming		
buildings (houses/churches)		

- Write a list to show what changed between the 1750s and 1830s. Then write a list to show what stayed the same. Think about transport, industry, farming and factories.

- Why do you think some things changed and others did not?
- What do you think might have caused some of these changes? (Clue: why were more houses needed?)

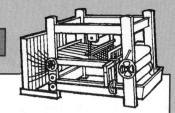

Key elements

Knowledge and understanding
- To consider factory conditions in the mid-nineteenth century, combining information from a written and pictorial source.

Key questions

- What were the dangers of working in a cotton factory?
- How were the workers treated? (Fines, overseer, whip, lack of safety guards, and so on.)

Background

Factories spread throughout Britain from 1771, especially in the North and Midlands, initially near sources of water power, and then coal. There were few government controls until 1833 when the Factory Act limited maximum weekly working hours to 48 (for 10–13 year-olds) and 69 (for 13–18 year-olds).

Factory inspectors were appointed and a minimum of two hours' daily education was required. Workers' salaries were very low, so wives and young children had to work in order to supplement family income. Safety was not a priority and accidents and fatalities were common.

New labour-saving machines resulted in cheap manufactured goods. Increasing overseas competition helped to keep wages down. The 1844 Factory Act limited the working day to 12 hours for women and children under 18, and six hours for children under 13. The 10-hour day was made law by the 1850 Act. The 1864 Factory Act extended government regulations beyond textiles and mining, and the 1867 Factory Act applied to all works employing over 50 workers.

Change and regulation was slow and piecemeal throughout this period, and was often ignored or avoided by unscrupulous owners. For example, some used the shift system to beat the maximum hour requirements.

Writing

- Write a letter to the government to complain about the working conditions in a cotton factory in the 1820s.
- Describe the difference between the overseer and the workers. How do you think the workers felt about this?
- Write a newspaper report about why you think there were very few safety measures in the factories.
- Imagine you have interviewed a young child who works in a factory. Explain why conditions for young children in factories were especially dangerous.

Activities

- The children should read the extract and compare the description with the illustration to discuss conditions in a cotton factory.
- The children could then discuss the process of weaving.
- Make a human weaving machine with 12 pupils to demonstrate the process of weaving. You will need one worker, four pairs of warps (holding thread tight), one shuttle and two arms (to push the shuttle backwards and forwards).

As the worker pushes arm A, arm A pushes the shuttle across the four warp pairs (two above, two below the shuttle). The shuttle takes cotton towards arm B. Arm B takes hold of the cotton while the shuttle stays still. Arms A and B push the weft towards the worker. The worker pushes arm B who then pushes the shuttle back towards arm A. Arm A takes hold of the cotton while the shuttle stays still. Arms A and B push the weft towards the worker.

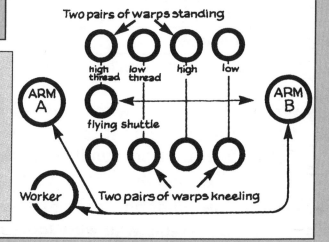

Factory conditions

● Look at this picture of a cotton factory in the 1840s.

● Read this passage about a cotton factory.

Factory conditions were harsh. Cotton workers in Manchester worked 14 hours a day in a temperature of 25°C, with only one hour's break. The factory door was locked and no drinks were allowed.

The worker earned less than £1.00 per week and could be fined 5p for opening a window, arriving late for work or whistling. Small children, aged five or younger, were sent under the machines to collect threads and cotton waste.

A man with a whip, called an overseer, beat the workers to make them work harder. The noise of the machines, the smell, the dust and the damp air, made the work unpleasant. The machines were dangerous, so accidents and deaths were common.

● Write a list of all the things that were unpleasant about working in a cotton factory.
● Why were small children employed?
● Why did the workers have short hair?

 ● Draw a factory poster asking for cotton workers. Describe the conditions and wages. Include a picture of workers in the factory.

The development of the mines –

Key elements

Historical enquiry
● To answer questions about nineteenth-century mining.

Knowledge and understanding
● To investigate the conditions in which children worked in coal mines up to 1842, and give some reasons for and effects of this work.

Key questions

● What were conditions like for young children working in coal mines up to 1842?
● Why were children employed in coal mines?

Writing

● Write a poem about a day working in a coal mine. Include ideas about working conditions and what children in the mines thought about their work.
● Imagine you work as a trapper or a drawer in a large mine. Write a letter to your cousin who works on a farm in the country. Explain carefully the job you have to do, why you have to do it and what it is like.
● Write a petition to parliament saying what is wrong with working conditions for children in the mines and how they could be made better.

Petition to Parliament
We the undersigned.....

Background

By 1850 coal output in Britain had reached 50 million tonnes per annum. This represented a 500% increase since 1800.

Demand for coal increased due to a number of factors:
– the growth in population and towns
– rapid industrialisation, notably of the iron and textiles industries, and the use of steam power
– the growth of railways
– the reduction in coal prices caused by improved transportation.

To meet this demand, deeper coal mines had to be sunk. This increased the dangers of flooding, explosion and collapse, and there were several tragedies. In 1866, 334 miners died in the Ardsley Oaks disaster.

Many miners died of lung disease, a direct consequence of breathing in coal dust. This was a common story: "My good man died nine years since with bad breath. He lingered some years and was entirely off work eleven years before he died."

In 1840, a Royal Commission reported on working conditions for children in the mines which led to the first of several Mines Acts. In 1842, children under ten were banned from working underground (increased to under twelve in 1860). In 1855, safety rules were drawn up. In 1872, site inspections were started.

Throughout the Victorian era, coal was the key fuel for powering industry and both inland and sea transport. It was also a major export.

Young children of my age were made to work in the mines.

They could be crushed or gassed.

The work was back-breaking, in horrible dark holes.

Activities

● Ask the children to read the extracts from the evidence given by children to the Royal Commission in 1840. Either discuss these extracts as a whole class activity or ask children to do this in pairs or small groups.
● Draw the children's attention to the points in the chart to help structure the discussion. Brainstorm ideas from the whole class or ask each group to report their ideas and write them on to a board or overhead projector.
● The children could then complete the chart using the information displayed to help them. This could be extended by discussing the dangers of mine work, including flooding, gas explosions, choke damp (carbon dioxide) and the collapse of workings and tunnels. The children could suggest ways in which mining could have been made safer.

The young miners

● Look at the pictures and read the passages.

A

I'm a trapper in the Gauber pit. I open and close a door called a 'trap'. I have to do it without a light and I'm scared. I go at four and sometimes half past three in the morning, and come out at five or later (at night). I never go to sleep. Sometimes I sing when I've a light but not in the dark; I dare not sing then. I don't like being in the pit.
(Sarah Gooder, a trapper aged eight.)

B

At the age of ten I became a drawer. I dragged coal through the mine. I wore a chain and girdle, I did not like it, it hurt me; it rubbed my skin off; I often felt pain. I got 15d (about 6p) each day. I had not time to eat a bit of meat from morning to night. I crawled on hands and feet. There was not room to stand.

A drawer, 1840.

● Copy and complete this chart:

	A trapper	A drawer
What was their age?		
How many hours did they work?		
How does their work make them feel?		

● Why do you think they do this work? Give two reasons.
● Describe the work of a trapper and a drawer. Write one sentence for each.
● Do you think you would like to have worked in a coal mine? Why?

Key elements

Historical enquiry
- To investigate the cholera outbreak in Soho, London in 1854.

Knowledge and understanding
- To demonstrate how and why attitudes towards disease may change.

Interpretations of history
- To consider the different views about the causes of the cholera epidemic in 1854 and why these different views were held.

Key questions

- According to Dr Snow, how did cholera spread in London in 1854?
- What other reasons were given for the epidemic at the time?

Writing

- Write a newspaper article about the epidemic as if you were living in London in 1860 – before Pasteur's germ theory was published.
- Imagine that you are a television reporter in London in the 1850s. Hold an interview with a child about cholera.

Background

Between 1831 and 1901 the population of the United Kingdom grew from 24.14 million to 41.54 million. At the same time, the proportion of the population living in towns and cities increased dramatically. Birmingham's population in 1841 was 202 000, but by 1901 this had grown to 760 000. Much of this growth was poorly planned and houses were built cheaply. The result was often large areas of slum dwellings, with poor drainage, unhygienic water supply and sewage systems.

Many industries dumped chemicals and waste directly into rivers already polluted by the untreated sewage from dwellings. Diseases such as typhoid, dysentery and cholera were spread from foul drinking water; typhus and infantile diarrhoea were spread by insects and vermin. Cholera was particularly unpleasant, causing diarrhoea and vomiting. If untreated, it led to death in two to three weeks. Sufferers further contaminated water supplies, passing the disease on to others. Coughing and sneezing spread tuberculosis, scarlet fever, whooping cough, diphtheria and measles. Poor diet and ventilation made problems worse, and conditions such as rickets and scurvy were common.

As a result of Chadwick's report in 1842, Boards of Health were established in many towns to raise money for drains and sewage disposal. The 1875 Public Health Act gave local authorities control over slum clearance and sewage disposal.

Improved scientific knowledge and the development of microscopes from the 1830s enabled Pasteur to develop his germ theory (1861). He proved that germs caused decay, and was followed in 1883 by Koch's discovery of the germ that causes cholera. These discoveries and other scientific advances enabled further improvements to be made.

Activities

- The children could compare the map and the written information on the newspaper page in order to identify the different reasons given for the epidemic.
- They could investigate and discuss the real cause of the epidemic of 1854.
- A class discussion could be held on how ideas and attitudes to disease gradually changed and how this was linked to increased scientific knowledge.

> People didn't know that germs caused diseases.

> Dr Snow showed that cholera could be traced to a dirty water pump.

Conditions in the towns

- You are a newspaper reporter working in 1854. Your job is to write a report about an outbreak of cholera in the Soho district of London.
- Read the information already on the page and use it to help you complete your report.

---

10 July 1854

Price: -/3d

LONDON TIMES

CHOLERA DEATHS IN SOHO

Opinions

Over 500 deaths in 10 days occurred around the Broad Street pump in the Soho district of London in 1854.

The map shows the main water pumps and deaths from cholera. I drew this map and then decided that bad water from one pump had spread the disease.

(Dr John Snow, who is investigating the causes of cholera)

The deaths were caused by cesspools (open toilets) and bad drains polluting the air.

(The Illustrated London News)

Facts

NEW IDEAS
Powerful microscopes

STOP PRESS
In 1861, Louis Pasteur proved that germs caused decay.

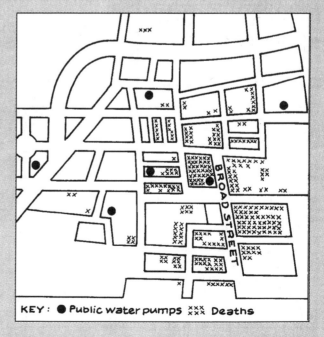

KEY: ● Public water pumps ✗✗✗ Deaths

Map of Soho area of central London, 1854

　　IDEAS BANK – *Victorian Britain*

Conditions in the countryside –

Key elements

Knowledge and understanding
- To examine the causes and effects of changes in the countryside between 1850 and 1900.

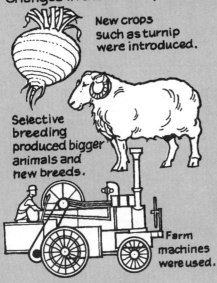

Changes in the countryside

New crops such as turnip were introduced.

Selective breeding produced bigger animals and new breeds.

Farm machines were used.

Key questions

- What caused changes in the countryside to occur?
- What was the effect of changes in the countryside?

Background

By 1837, most farming land in England was enclosed. Land used to be split into smaller plots and strips, and was usually farmed to produce food for individuals. It was now grouped together and fenced, allowing farmers to produce food to sell. These farmers either owned the land they farmed, or more usually they were tenant farmers.

The effect of this was that farming became a lucrative business. New methods, techniques and machines were introduced to increase yields. Less land was left fallow (without a crop), new crops like turnips were introduced, and selective breeding was used to increase the size of animals.

However, a number of problems arose. The poor often lost their land. They had to rely on wages – but agriculture employed fewer people. Many farm workers were provided with housing as part of their payment. This effectively tied them to the land.

Farming enjoyed a boom between 1850 and the mid- to late 1860s. The growth of the railway system opened up new markets for farm produce and the growing population of towns and cities provided increased demand. However, after 1870, a period of depression started. Farmers at home could not compete with food imported from abroad. The first imports were wheat from North America. After the invention of canning and refrigeration in the 1880s, cheap meat and dairy products soon followed. Foreign competition and improved technology was to further reduce the number of jobs available in the countryside. This led to rural depopulation and a decline in the importance of farming.

In 1837, farming and land ownership was the most important part of the economy. Over 80% of the population lived in the countryside and worked in agriculture. By 1900 a huge change had taken place. Most people lived in towns and cities and worked in industry. The focus of the nation's economy was trade, industry and Empire.

Activities

- The children could make a display showing changes in the countryside.
- Explain to them what imports are. Do all farm imports have a bad effect on farmers? Mention tea from India and cotton from the southern states of the USA.
- Ask them if the changes in the countryside have continued in Britain since 1900. Ask them to look at food labels when they get home.
- As an extension activity they could produce a display showing how farm machines or cheap imports affect farm workers.

Daily Blah

FARM WORKERS LOSE JOBS

CITY

Writing

- Write a newspaper report describing the changes that occurred to the countryside between 1850 and 1900. Explain what you think the effects of these changes would be on the lives of those living in Tolbury.

Changes in the countryside

The population of Tolbury has grown to 20 000. The land supplies food to the growing town. Farmers can use the roads and new railway to get crops into town. Some farmers have not bought the new machinery, and still employ lots of farmhands.

Farmer B (1900)

Tolbury has continued to grow. There are now 40 000 people living there. There is more demand for food. Farmers have been badly hit by imports of cheap wheat from America. They all use farm machinery and lots of farmhands are unemployed.

- Why is farmer A pleased? Give two reasons.
- Why were new roads and railways important to farming in 1850?
- Why do you think people wanted to live in towns like Tolbury?
- What problems does farmer B have in 1900?
- Copy and complete a chart like this. Include as many changes as you can.

Changes between 1850 and 1900	Good for farmers	Bad for farmers	Reason why
1. Towns grew larger			More people meant that farmers could sell more food.

- Find out why wheat imports from America were bad news for farmers in Britain.

Improvements in living conditions – Ideas page

Key elements

Knowledge and understanding
- To describe and identify reasons for and results of improvements in public health in the mid-nineteenth century.

Organisation and communication
- To select and organise information about public health and present it in a structured form.

Key questions

- How important was cost in the improvement of public health?
- How important was government influence in the improvement of public health?
- Why was the advice of doctors sometimes ignored?

Background

As towns grew, no-one took responsibility for public health and town planning. Local authorities had limited power and little money. Parliament was reluctant to interfere with the freedom of property owners.

Chadwick's Report of 1842 revealed widespread overcrowding, lack of proper drainage and sewage disposal and the absence of fresh running water. The 1848 Public Health Act allowed local authorities to set up boards of health on a voluntary basis. The 1875 Public Health Act established minimum sanitation standards with a nationwide system of sewage disposal, drainage, street cleaning and fresh water supplies monitored by health inspectors.

The Artisans Dwellings Act of 1875 permitted councils to clear away slum districts (again on a voluntary basis). Also, a national system to dispose of sewage and provide clean water was implemented. The 1888 Local Government Act set up elected county councils, giving wide powers to the local community. In 1890, the first local authority housing was built, assisted by government grants. From 1894, parish and district councils were elected and given responsibilities.

Public health began as piecemeal and voluntary, gradually becoming a nationwide network administered by publically elected authorities.

Writing

- Hold your own public health meeting in the classroom and write a report about it.
- Imagine you lived in Newtown in 1848. Write a letter to the government asking for help and advice.

Improving public health

1. Better and bigger hospitals.

2. Improve hygiene.

3. Find the causes and cures of diseases.

Activities

- Role play: organise a class debate to consider the issues of improving public health.
- The children could cut up and shuffle the main views on the activity sheet and then decide whether they are for or against a Board of Health.
- The children could investigate other issues relating to the improvement of public health, such as the importance of spending money or whether help and advice was needed for the government.

Public meeting

In 1848, the people of Newtown met to discuss setting up the Board of Health to deal with dirt and disease.

Public Meeting
Town Hall
Newtown
8 o'clock tonight

FOR A BOARD OF HEALTH	AGAINST A BOARD OF HEALTH

I have seen the dirt and filth in the slums. These conditions spread disease. We can't let all these people die.

Doctor Mortimer.

Who's going to pay for all this street cleaning, sewage disposal and fresh water supplies? It's the factory owners who pay.

Mr Gallagher, factory owner.

I want my workers to be fit and healthy to do a good day's work. Give them sewers and fresh water.

Mr Hepplewhite, factory owner.

We built Newtown by hard work and money. Why should we be told what to do by doctors and officials?

Sir Dudley Ramshaw, landowner.

With clean water and clean streets you can keep people healthier. They will live longer. Not so many babies will die.

Mr Jarvis, the health inspector.

What do doctors know anyway? All these new ideas. Where's the proof? How do they know that overcrowding causes disease?

Lord Newtown.

Everybody, rich and poor, will benefit from clean water and sewage disposal.

Mr MacDuff, the engineer.

I run a small grocer shop. I work very hard. I can't afford to pay any more taxes.

Mr Clementine, the grocer.

I help the orphans in the workhouse. Their fathers and mothers died after drinking dirty water.

Reverend Hindmarsh.

You can't change the habits of these common people. They'll always be dirty.

Lady Newtown.

- Write a report about setting up a Board of Health. Write about:
  - the arguments in favour
  - the arguments against.

- Imagine you lived in Newtown in 1848. Write about your views.
- Who else would you have invited to this meeting? Why?

Steam power – Ideas page

Steam ship

Key elements

Knowledge and understanding
- To demonstrate factual knowledge about the use of steam power.
- To describe some of the advantages of new technology.

Stephenson's Rocket

Key questions

- What did a steam locomotive look like?
- What fuel did steam engines use?
- What was the source of power?

Background

Steam power was developed well before 1837, but it remained virtually the only form of power throughout the Victorian era. It was a key factor in Britain's industrialisation.

The first steam engine was designed by a Frenchman named Denis Papin in 1690. Thomas Savery built a similar engine eight years later. However, in 1706, Thomas Newcomen designed a steam engine that could be used to drain mines. James Watt and Matthew Boulton improved Newcomen's engine and patented it in 1775. It enabled a wheel to be turned by a steam engine and made it theoretically possible to use steam to power a vehicle for the first time.

In 1802, Richard Trevithick patented a high-pressure steam engine (by using high pressure the engine could be greatly reduced in size and weight). In 1804, he made the first trial run of the first ever steam locomotive. Many mines already using horse-drawn 'railways' showed great interest in this new idea, and engineers such as George Stephenson, William Hedley and John Blenkinsop concentrated their efforts on improving performance and reliability.

In 1829 trials were held at Rainhill to choose the best locomotive for a new railway built to connect the industrial city of Manchester to the port of Liverpool. The famous *Rocket* built by George and his son Robert Stephenson won the day. In the next 20 years railways spread across the land.

Activities

- The children could investigate how steam engines work and how they were used to drive locomotives.
- They could also explore different attitudes to the development of steam power and then role-play their findings.
- Ask the children to find out why the use of steam power has now declined.

WHY STEAM POWER DECLINED

- ✳ It is dirtier and less efficient than newer types of power.
- ✳ Steam engines are too heavy for cars and planes.
- ✳ They need too much coal and water

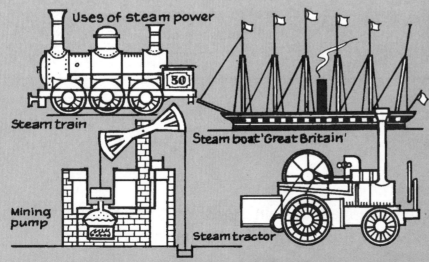
Uses of steam power

Steam train

Steam boat 'Great Britain'

Mining pump

Steam tractor

Writing

- Imagine you are setting up a railway company. Write a notice to explain to people why steam locomotives are better than horse transport.
- Write a newspaper report about the 1829 trials at Rainhill and the *Rocket*.

Steam power

- Cut out the diagram below and stick it onto a sheet of thin card. Construct your steam engine.

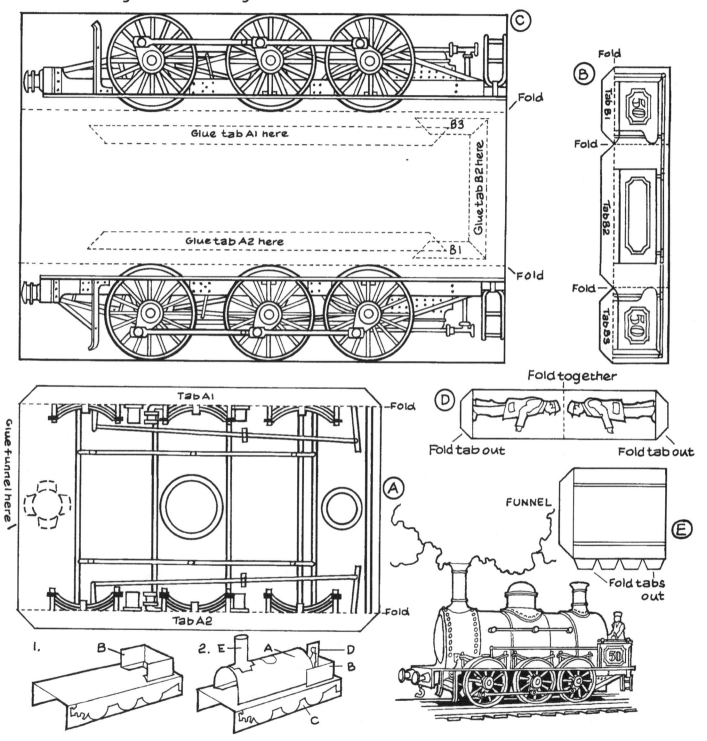

- Imagine you are trying to sell your steam engine. Design a poster to advertise it.
- Write a speech to describe the advantages of your steam engine over horse-drawn coaches. Use your model to help you.

Key elements

Interpretations of history
- To make deductions from pictures of rail travel.
- To identify different interpretations of rail travel.

Historical enquiry
- To investigate and review the characteristics of railway travel.

Knowledge and understanding
- To compare Victorian rail travel with today.

Key questions

- What was rail travel like for the Victorians?

Background

The technology of railways developed from the use of steam engines in coal mines. Various engineers such as Trevithick, Stephenson and Brunel were involved, changing the method of pulling wagons on tracks from fixed steam engines on the ground to smaller steam locomotives.

The Rainhill trials in 1829 and the subsequent opening of the Liverpool to Manchester railway in 1830 heralded considerable railway building throughout the 1840s and 1850s. 'Railway mania' was developed by rival companies, financed by share speculation. Many unnecessary duplicate lines were built which proved uneconomic. In 1846, a standard railway gauge was adopted – except the GWR (Great Western Railway, designed by Isambard Kingdom Brunel) which maintained a broad gauge until 1892.

By 1850, Britain was the only country in the world to have a network of railways stretching throughout the country. This brought progress and prosperity, increased trade and job opportunities, encouraged tourism and improved communications. On the other hand, many people feared railways would destroy the countryside and village life, causing pollution and loss of life.

Railways influenced the social and economic lives of everyone. They enabled the growth of suburbs around most major cities and towns, and remained the most important form of transport until the opening of the first motorways in the 1960s.

Activities

- Hold a classroom discussion: what is a railway like today? Describe the differences under the categories given in the table on the activity page.
- The children could explore the differences between rail travel in Victorian Britain and different forms of travel today, including cars, buses and aeroplanes.
- Ask the children to think about whether the pictures on the activity page are reliable historical sources. Do they show one person's idea, rather than the reality? Do they exaggerate or generalise? More able children could try to find evidence to support or contradict the ideas in these pictures.

Writing

- Using the information from the activity page, list some good and bad points about travelling by railway in the Victorian era.
- Do you think these pictures are a good advertisement for travelling by railway? Explain your answer by writing a newspaper report to go with the pictures.

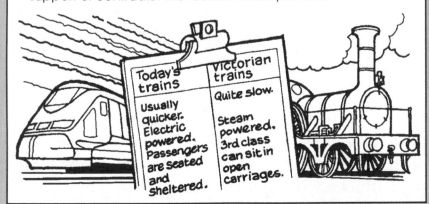

IDEAS BANK – *Victorian Britain* © Folens (not copiable)

Travelling by railway

● Look at the pictures showing the three classes of railway travel.

FIRST CLASS

SECOND CLASS

WORD BOX
rushed
cold
squashed
open
noisy
spacious
crowded
calm
large
few
many
small

THIRD CLASS

● Copy and complete the chart below. Write one word in each space. Use the word box to help you.
● Use the information in your chart to describe the differences between the different classes of rail travel.

Travelling by railway	1st class	2nd class	3rd class
1. Number of passengers			
2. Description of carriages			
3. Behaviour of passengers			
4. Comfort			

● Why do you think people were separated into three classes?
● Do you think these pictures give a true picture of what it was like to travel by train? Explain your answer.

IDEAS BANK – *Victorian Britain*

The age of inventions – Ideas page

Key elements

Historical enquiry
- To investigate pictures of Victorian inventions and make deductions from them.

Organisation and communication
- To describe understanding of the inventions.

Key questions

- What kind of devices were invented in the Victorian Era?
- What part did new inventions play in people's lives?

Background

Industrialisation and the growth in technology, combined with the expansion of railways in the 1830s and 1840s and the rapid growth of urban populations, provided both the means of producing consumer goods and the demand for them. Many of these goods were products of the iron, textiles, ceramics and chemical industries which developed between 1760 and 1890.

The Great Exhibition of 1851 provided a shop window to the world, when all types of people flocked to marvel at the goods on display. The age of consumerism had begun, with much of this development relying upon both inventions and innovation.

However, by the end of the Victorian era, the economies of rivals such as Germany and the United States were outperforming Britain. Instead of recapturing the innovation and inventiveness of the early Industrial Revolution by retraining and investing, the British economy, artificially cushioned by her world Empire, began to slip behind.

Activities

- Working in small groups, the children should attempt to match the pictures with the correct description. The answers are:
  1. The ice pricker
  2. Ice spatula and pail
  3. Bomb moulds
  4. The sausage machine
  5. The egg cutter
  6. The ice cream freezer
- The children could then produce a display using these pictures and written descriptions.
- Each group could give a short presentation, explaining their choice of invention.
- Extension activities could include investigating other inventions of the Victorian era and the part they played in people's lives.

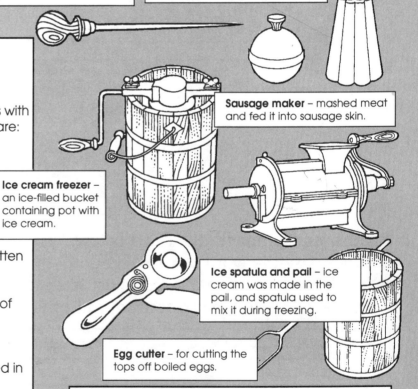

Ice pricker – used to break up blocks of ice.

Bomb moulds – used to coat ice cream with different layers.

Sausage maker – mashed meat and fed it into sausage skin.

Ice cream freezer – an ice-filled bucket containing pot with ice cream.

Ice spatula and pail – ice cream was made in the pail, and spatula used to mix it during freezing.

Egg cutter – for cutting the tops off boiled eggs.

Gramophone (1877)

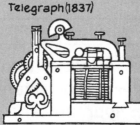

Telegraph (1837)

Writing

- Write a short description for each picture, explaining carefully how the inventions work.
- Write a diary entry for a Victorian boy or girl, describing how excited you are that your parents have just bought one of these inventions. Describe what it is and what it does.

The age of inventions

● Match each picture to the correct name.

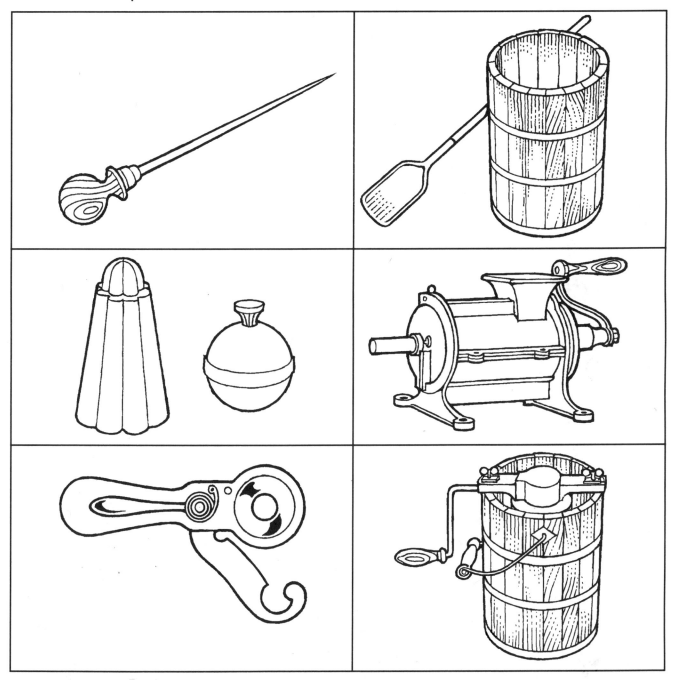

The sausage machine	The egg cutter	The ice cream freezer
The ice pricker	Ice spatula and pail	Bomb moulds

 NOW

● Choose one invention and describe carefully how you think it worked.
● Describe how you think each invention would have changed people's lives in Victorian Britain.

The Great Exhibition – Ideas page

Key elements

Organisation and communication
- To select, organise and present information about the Great Exhibition of 1851.

Knowledge and understanding
- To explore specific details of the Great Exhibition and explain what they reveal about the Victorian era.

Background

Prince Albert led a Royal Commission to plan a 'Great Exhibition' in London in 1851. The aim of this exhibition was to display the latest industrial, scientific and artistic achievements from all over the world and to provide British goods with a showcase. Leading 'Free Traders' (people in favour of trade without customs duties) like Gladstone fully supported the venture.

A site in Hyde Park was selected and a huge glass exhibition hall, designed by Joseph Paxton, was erected. This became known as the Crystal Palace. The building was moved to the present-day Crystal Palace site in South Kensington after the Exhibition and was burned down in November 1936.

7381 British and 6556 overseas exhibitors showed off their wares in the Crystal Palace. The Queen herself opened the Exhibition on 1 May 1851 and commented, "God bless my dear country which has shown itself so great today". In little over five months, six million people from all over the world visited the site. The Great Exhibition had been a great success.

Key questions

- What types of products were displayed at the Great Exhibition in 1851?
- What do these products tell us about life in the Victorian era?

Writing

- Write a newspaper report from the Great Exhibition, describing some of the things you have seen.
- Write a letter from Queen Victoria to Prince Albert saying how much you enjoyed the Exhibition.

Activities

- After they have answered the questions, the children could investigate other examples of textiles, ceramics, glass and wrought iron that are not included on the activity page.
- They could also investigate other areas of the Exhibition that illustrate life in the Victorian era, such as fashion and jewellery.
- Extension activities could include exploring whether there have been any modern-day equivalents to the Great Exhibition.

Modern Great Exhibitions –
Birmingham International Motor Show
–
World Trade Fair
–
Gateshead Flower Festival

The Great Exhibition

These pictures show four exhibits from the Great Exhibition of 1851.
● Look carefully at the pictures and answer the questions.

Textiles
● Describe this pattern. Draw your own version of it and design curtains for a Victorian home.
● Are patterns like this still used in homes today?

Ceramics
● Describe this tea service carefully. Do you like it? Why?
● Do people still use cups and saucers like this today?

Wrought iron
● Sketch a section of this gate and describe the designs used.
● Use these ideas to design a gate for your school.

Glass
● Describe this stained glass window and explain what it shows.
● Are windows like this still used today?

● Find out more about the Great Exhibition.
● Design your own exhibition for your classroom.

Key elements

Knowledge and understanding
- To consider the characteristic working-class day at the seaside.
- To consider how these activities reflected the ideas, beliefs and attitudes of Victorian people in the past.

Key questions

- What were the different activities for day-trippers on a visit to the seaside?
- How different are these activities from days out today?
- What attitudes and behaviour were acceptable to the working class but not to the middle or upper classes?

Background

The working classes worked for about 300 days in the year and could not afford holidays. They rested on the 52 Sundays, but found museums and most parks closed. Only the public houses and churches remained open. This left about 12 days for holidays, usually unpaid (including Bank Holidays).

The rail network provided cheap day returns to the countryside and seaside. Brighton, Margate, Blackpool and Skegness became popular for 'day-trippers'. Seaside towns grew as the lower-middle classes rented a boarding house for a fortnight. Southend grew rapidly from the 1880s (a population of 8000 in 1881 grew to over 12 000 by 1892). Rich Victorians found more 'select' seaside towns to visit in August, such as Bournemouth, away from the day-trippers.

At first, day-trippers had retained some respectability. There were separate beaches for males and females alighting from bathing machines. By the 'Naughty Nineties', mixed bathing was common and the bathing machines had gone (see poster, below). Tourism developed as the seaside towns catered for the needs of the visitors. Dances and shows ended in time to catch the last train to London.

Bathing machines and bathers

POST CARD

Dear Jim,
I've been swimming, watching Punch and Judy and to the Fun Fair. It's great.
from Sarah

Jim Jones,
4 Dock Lane,
Gravesend,
Kent.

Writing

- Imagine you are on a day-trip to Southend in 1886. Write a postcard to a friend telling them all about your day.
- Write a detailed description of one of the activities from the game for a wall display.

Southend poster

Activities

- The activity sheet should be enlarged to A3 size.
- The children could display writing and pictures of their own favourite day out.
- They could produce a class exhibition by choosing one of the squares from the game and producing writing and pictures to go with it.
- Extension activities could include investigating the different leisure activities of the upper, middle and lower classes in Victorian Britain.

Leisure

- Work in pairs or small groups to discover what happened on your day out in Southend. You will need dice and counters.
- Keep a record of your day out as a diary.
- Explain what you think you would most enjoy.

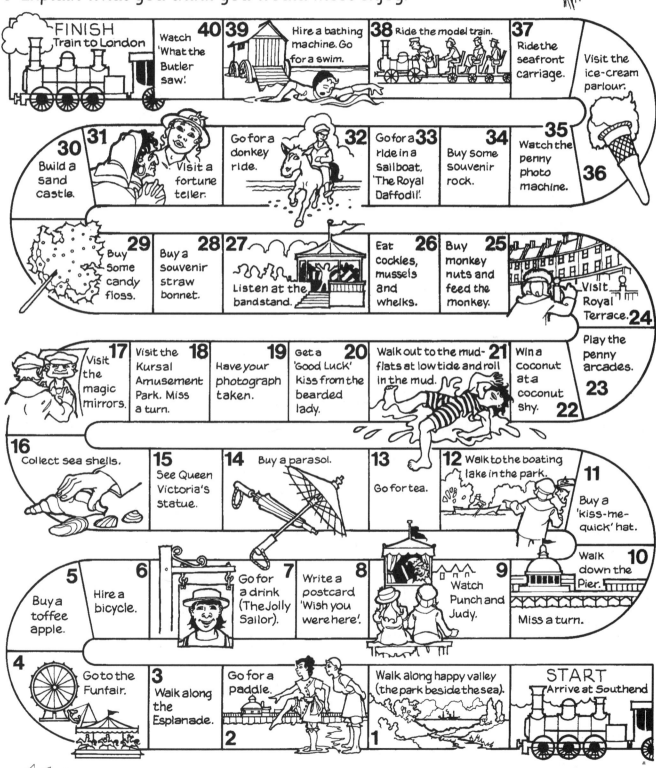

FINISH Train to London

40 Watch 'What the Butler saw'.

39 Hire a bathing machine. Go for a swim.

38 Ride the model train.

37 Ride the seafront carriage.

Visit the ice-cream parlour.

30 Build a sand castle.

31 Visit a fortune teller.

32 Go for a donkey ride.

33 Go for a ride in a sailboat, 'The Royal Daffodil'.

34 Buy some souvenir rock.

35 Watch the penny photo machine.

36

29 Buy some candy floss.

28 Buy a souvenir straw bonnet.

27 Listen at the bandstand.

26 Eat cockles, mussels and whelks.

25 Buy monkey nuts and feed the monkey.

Visit Royal Terrace. **24**

17 Visit the magic mirrors.

18 Visit the Kursal Amusement Park. Miss a turn.

19 Have your photograph taken.

20 Get a 'Good Luck' kiss from the bearded lady.

21 Walk out to the mud-flats at low tide and roll in the mud.

22 Win a coconut at a coconut shy.

Play the penny arcades. **23**

16 Collect sea shells.

15 See Queen Victoria's statue.

14 Buy a parasol.

13 Go for tea.

12 Walk to the boating lake in the park.

11 Buy a 'kiss-me-quick' hat.

5 Buy a toffee apple.

6 Hire a bicycle.

7 Go for a drink (The Jolly Sailor).

8 Write a postcard 'Wish you were here'.

9 Watch Punch and Judy.

10 Walk down the Pier. Miss a turn.

4 Go to the Funfair.

3 Walk along the Esplanade.

2 Go for a paddle.

1 Walk along happy valley (the park beside the sea).

START Arrive at Southend

NOW ● Write about one special day out that you have had.

Key elements

Knowledge and understanding
- To consider the way of life of the English upper classes and to contrast this with the life of a servant (pages 30–31).

A nanny with a young lord

Key questions

- What kind of life did a rich person lead in Victorian Britain?
- How was this life different to that of a servant?

Background

There was a huge gulf between the way of life of the upper and lower classes in Victorian Britain. A poor boy started school at five or six in a class of 60–80 pupils. By the age of ten, he spent half the day at school and the other half at work. When he was 12, he went to work full-time.

A typical rich boy had a nanny to look after him and saw his parents for half-an-hour each day, usually after tea. He had his own private tutor or governess. At the age of 12, he went to public school (Eton, Harrow, Rugby or Winchester). These schools were famous for bullying rather than for academic achievement (see *Tom Brown's Schooldays* by Thomas Hughes for a description of Rugby school). Rich girls usually remained at home and were taught how to sing, sew, paint and make polite conversation.

After public school, the boys went to university, notably Oxford and Cambridge, where there was an active social life rather than a serious programme of study. After university, a 'gentleman' might consider going into the Church, the army or politics. Otherwise he enjoyed a wide social life. From November to January, he toured Europe to avoid the cold, damp English winters, possibly exploring the historic ruins of the Romans, Greeks or Egyptians. From February to April he retired to his country house for hunting. May, June and July was the main season in London for balls, theatres, dinners and parties. In August, he might visit the seaside and in September and October he would shoot grouse, pheasants or stags in Scotland. The social cycle then began again.

Some wealthy people did devote themselves to work in business, industry and commerce. A few became famous scientists, archaeologists, engineers or explorers.

Victorian rich child	Victorian poor child	Myself
I have a governess. I have a nanny.	I go to charity school. I work at the mill.	I go to junior school. I play with friends.

Activities

- Ask the children to read the extracts of the imaginary life of Lord Frampton. Discuss the merits of each activity and divide them between the good points (those that helped other people and society) and the bad points (those that only helped himself, such as selfish enjoyment).
- Organise a 'This is your life' involving ten pupils (eight guests, the presenter and Lord Frampton or another historical figure). This may involve costume and drama. It may be a suitable activity to video. The rest of the class could be involved in the planning and production of the role-play.
- When the children have worked through the activity page on the life of a servant (page 31), they could compare and contrast the lives of rich people and servants in Victorian Britain.

Writing

- Draw a chart comparing a rich child and a poor child in Victorian times and yourself.
- Imagine you are one of the people talking about Lord Frampton on the activity page. Write a description of a day you have spent with the Lord, including what you did and what he was like.

The life of a lord

- Read what these people say about Lord Frampton.

He was leader of the hunt. He led the hounds to the fox at least three times a week during February, March and April. His favourite cry was "tally-ho, Basil".

Captain Spilling, Master of the hounds.

He went on family seaside holidays each summer to Frinton, Essex. He had the biggest bathing hut on the beach.

Madge, the bathing hut attendant.

He once took a group of friends out in the midday sun around the ruins of Pompeii in Italy. He insisted on everyone being dressed smartly.

Mr Brown, the valet.

He spoke for four hours about the evils of child labour and the importance of education, in his first speech in the House of Lords.

Lord Ryton

He went to Eton Public School and enjoyed learning Latin and Greek. He was often beaten by masters and prefects.

Lord Allen, fellow Etonian

He built the box pews in the estate church and paid for the stained-glass window in honour of his late father.

Reverend Wildey

He was the first man in the county to install one of Mr Crapper's toilets. He later installed gas lighting in his country house.

Viscount Frampton

He danced me off my feet at the first ball of the London season and said that my ball gown was the finest that he had seen.

Lady Frampton

- Draw a chart like the one below and fill in all the good points and bad points about Lord Frampton.

Good points	Bad points

- Organise a 'This is your life'. Ask eight members of your class to talk about a person from the past. You need an announcer to run the programme and introduce the guests. The guests could dress up in costume.

Key elements

Knowledge and understanding
- To understand the hierarchy of servants and the team work needed to run an upper-class Victorian household.
- To contrast this with the way of life of the English upper classes.

Key questions

- What kind of lives did Victorian servants lead?
- How was this life different to that of a rich person?
- Why did the servants have their own hierarchy?

Background

Most upper-class and middle-class Victorian families had at least one servant or maid. A large country house had between eight and forty servants. They were paid a small wage and had board and lodging. Their quarters were in the attic or the basement. They kept away from the family, using separate staircases and entrances. They ate in the kitchen and had to be quiet at all times.

They often had to face the wall if they saw the family approaching. The Duke of Portland would sack any housemaid that he met in the corridor. On the other hand, Sir Harry Featherstonhaugh married his dairymaid in 1825.

The servants could be summoned by the family at any time of the day or night by a system of bells. The staff of a large country house were divided into 'lower' and 'upper' servants according to their status. Servants were separated according to gender, with different sleeping areas. At Lanhydrock in Cornwall, they also had different staircases.

The 1881 Census revealed that over 10% of all females over five years old were employed as indoor servants.

Comparing lord and servant	
Lord	Servant
✳ Gives out orders. ✳ Can behave in any way he chooses.	✳ Always follows orders. ✳ Must be quiet and stay out of the way.

Activities

- Divide the children into groups. Each group needs one copy of the plan of the house and one set of cards.
- They should cut out the cards and place them face up in the centre of their group. The teacher then reads out the following statements, one at a time, allowing the children to discuss and place the cards in the appropriate room of the house.
- The children could compare and contrast the life of a servant with that of a rich person (pages 28–29).

Writing

- Write an imaginary conversation with four different servants in a Victorian household, describing their daily routine, their work, their hopes and anxieties. This could be written and acted out as a play.

Statements (room number in brackets)
Nanny: I get the children dressed, feed them and play with them in the nursery. (1)
Footman: I carry the coal, clean the shoes, and I wait at table. (8)
Scullery maid: Cook shouted at me today as I took too long peeling the potatoes. (9)
Housemaid: I must get the fire lit in the sitting room before the family comes downstairs. (6)
Lady's maid: I must remember to wake up my lady earlier this morning because it takes so long to brush her hair. (3)

Cook: The housekeeper tells me that I will need to prepare a large dinner party as there is a family celebration next week. (10)
Valet: I must lay out the master's clothes and polish his buttons before he changes for dinner. (4)
Housekeeper: I must discuss menus for the week with the mistress in the drawing room. (7)
Chambermaid: The housekeeper has told me that I must make all the beds today. (2)
Butler: The master has summoned me to the living room to discuss stocking the wine cellar. (5)

The life of a servant

- Cut out the cards and place them face up in the centre of the group.
- Your teacher will read out statements from each servant. After each one is read out, place a card into the correct empty box in the house.
- When you have filled up all 10 boxes, the first person to call out 'Housey' is the winner. Good luck!

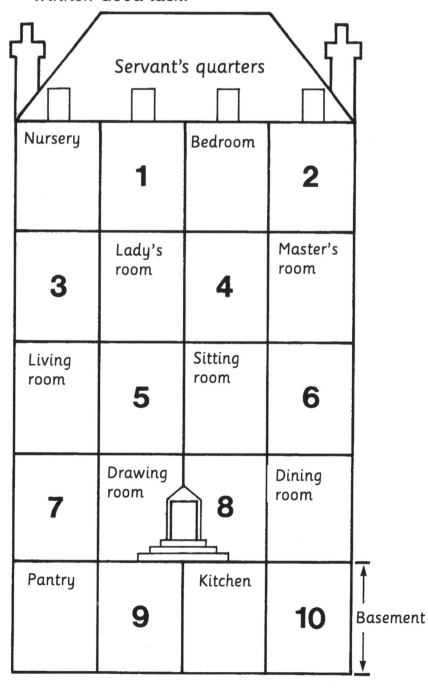

SCULLERY MAID — Washes and prepares the food for the cook. Washes up.

LADY'S MAID — Cares for the clothes and appearance of the lady of the house.

NANNY — Looks after the children.

CHAMBERMAID — Cleans bedrooms using a duster and broom.

HOUSEKEEPER — Keeps a record of all spending.

FOOTMAN — Carries the coal. Cleans the shoes. Waits at table.

VALET — Cares for clothes and appearance of the master of the house.

BUTLER — In charge of the staff and wine cellar. Waits at table.

COOK — Shops for food. Cooks all meals. In charge of the scullery maid.

HOUSEMAID — Lights the fires. Cleans the living rooms.

Key elements

Knowledge and understanding
- To learn about the main characteristics of Victorian fashion.
- To discover how fashion was influenced by Victorian attitudes.

Chronology
- To place styles of dress in correct chronological order.

Key questions

- What were fashions like for men and women in Victorian Britain?
- How did these fashions change during the Victorian period?

paisley shawl

gloves

bustle

wide dress with bamboo/ whalebone frame

Writing

- You have been asked by Lord and Lady Boswell to design clothes for the summer season in 1875. Write a description of a new outfit. You could include diagrams and sketches.

Background

With the growth of industry in Victorian Britain came prosperity for the upper classes and the growing middle class. They spent more on fashionable clothes.

Women's dresses were colourful and elaborate. Skirts became wider with many petticoats, often held out by a frame of bamboo, whale bone or metal. By 1840, paisley shawls were very popular. Gloves were worn to keep the hands soft and white. Bustles became fashionable from the 1870s to 1890s.

Men's clothes looked respectable and were usually in dark colours. Men's styles varied little during the Victorian period: they wore waisted coats, trousers with straps under the instep of the boot, and top hats. Hair was long and curly with sideburns and moustaches. Striped trousers and morning coats were popular. Less formal attire was permitted for sporting occasions, such as tweed lounge suits and a variety of caps including the Derby, Straw Boater and Tam O'Shanter (see illustration below).

Children were dressed in unisex clothes until they were four or five years old, then they were dressed as miniature adults. These formal clothes restricted play.

Fashion was mainly for the rich and well-off. They reflected the rich Victorian's life of relaxation, while poorer people could rarely afford such luxuries.

Tam O'Shanter

Straw boater

Derby or bowler hat

Activities

- Discuss with the children when men and women would have worn these fashions. Ask them what items would be included with them.
- The children could cut out the pictures, placing them in the correct chronological order, and stick the correct caption underneath each one.
- Hold a class discussion.
  – Who could afford to be fashionable?
  – How did fashion reflect the Victorians, ideas about morality? (Especially for women, who could not even expose ankles.)
  – How far did fashion reflect the lifestyle of rich Victorians? (A life of leisure.)
  – Do the fashions change? Does this reflect changing times? (Ladies wore trousers for cycling).
- The children could organise a Victorian fashion show based on the information supplied on the activity page.

Fashion

Look at these ladies in fashionable Victorian dresses.
- Match the captions to the correct picture.

| Waisted dress with bamboo frame. Bare shoulders. 1840 | Dress swept up to the back to form a waterfall of frills. 1874 | Waisted figure-hugging dress. Pleated sleeves and hem. 1899 | Ballooned pantaloons with wide collar and puffed sleeves. 1895 |

Look at these gentlemen in fashionable Victorian clothes.
- Match the captions to the correct picture.

| Evening dress with tailed coat. Frilled shirt, bow tie and cape. 1837 | Informal suit worn with spats and bowler hat. 1881 | Formal wear with greatcoat, waistcoat, bow-tie, top hat. 1881 | Country wear. Caped belted coat and deerstalker hat. 1885 |

 • Design and draw an outfit that you would like to have worn in Victorian Britain.

Education – Ideas page

Key elements

Knowledge and understanding
- To explore the main characteristics of Victorian education.
- To compare Victorian education with today.

Historical enquiry
- To investigate the characteristics of a Victorian classroom.

Key questions

- How were Victorian children taught?
- What are the main similarities and differences between education today and during the Victorian era?

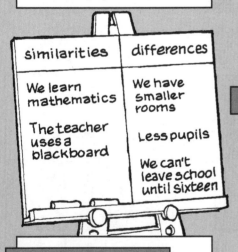

similarities	differences
We learn mathematics	We have smaller rooms
The teacher uses a blackboard	Less pupils
	We can't leave school until sixteen

Writing

- Write a poem to describe a typical day for a pupil at a London Board school in 1883.
- Imagine you are a school inspector visiting a Board school like the one in the photograph. Write a report about your visit, saying what you think is good and bad about the school.

Background

At the beginning of the Victorian period, the standard of education was poor and varied. The children of the rich were educated in fee-paying public and grammar schools. Most poor children did not go to school, although charity schools taught some children the basic skills. The 1870 Education Act established Board schools for children from five to 12 years old; a small fee was charged until 1891. Until 1918, many of these children worked in factories before and after school.

Between 1870 and 1900, the school-leaving age was raised from 10 to 12 years of age. Schools were free to organise their classes by age or ability. Often children of different ages were taught in classes of up to 50 pupils. Teaching was often very formal and discipline was harsh.

maths tables

$1 \times 7 = 7$
$2 \times 7 = 14$
$3 \times 7 = 21$
$4 \times 7 = 28$
$5 \times 7 = 35$
$6 \times$
$7 \times$
$8 \times$
9×7
10×7
11×7
$12 \times 7 =$

bell

blackboard

dunce cap

cane

slate

chalk

Activities

- The children could compare the photograph of the Board school with their own classroom for differences and similarities. They could brainstorm their ideas or divide into groups for a set period and then report back.
- Discuss 'rote learning'. Ask the children to say the 'seven times' table out loud five times. They could then discuss whether they would like this to be the only method by which they are taught. They could also discuss teaching methods that are used today.
- In small groups, the children could investigate and discuss the items found in a Victorian classroom, including rows of desks, slates, blackboard, chalk, maps or a globe, dunces caps, stick and a bell.
- The children could organise a Victorian classroom and re-enact a lesson, including:
  - changing modern names to Old Testament names or virtues (such as Honesty or Charity)
  - using old words, such as 'thee' and 'hast'
  - using 'major' and 'minor' to denote siblings
  - re-enforcing hands in the air and standing up when answering questions.

Education

● Look carefully at this photograph of a Victorian classroom in 1883.

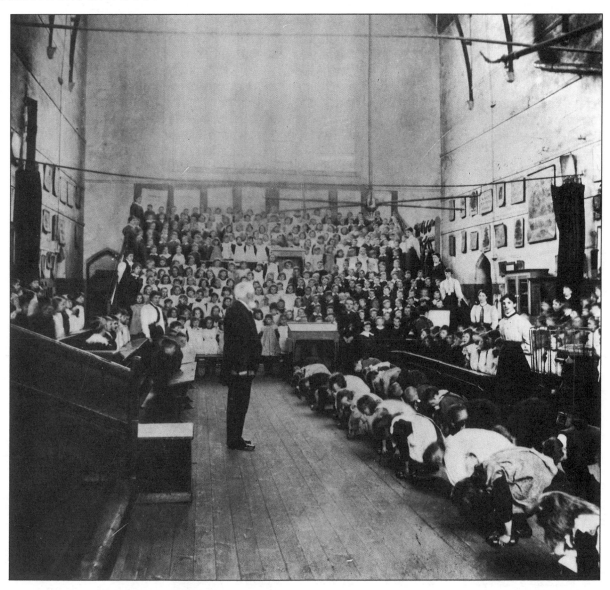

● In what way is this school different to yours? Think about:
  – the size of the room
  – the number of children
  – the ages of the children
  – what the children are doing
  – what the teacher is doing.

● Is there any way in which this school is the same as yours? How?

  ● Find out about some of the things that could be found in a Victorian classroom. Draw or describe some of them.
  ● Do you think education was good or bad for Victorian children? Write a list of good things and a list of bad things.

London street life – Ideas page

Key elements

Knowledge and understanding
- To investigate life in Victorian London and the different jobs available.

Organisation and communication
- To select and present information about life on London streets in the 1860s.

Key questions

- What were the main characteristics of London street life in the Victorian era?
- What differences are there to London today?

Background

The growth of towns is one of the main characteristics of the Victorian era. Cities such as Manchester, Glasgow, Birmingham, Leeds and Liverpool rapidly increased in size due to rising population, agricultural changes that resulted in fewer jobs in the countryside, Irish immigration and the growth of factories.

London developed as a communications, trading and commercial centre. It became the centre of a growing railway network, linking many parts of Britain to the capital city. Grand railway stations were built, such as Paddington, Euston and St Pancras, which looked impressive and thus encouraged people to travel by train. Large docks handled imports from all over the world.

Hotels and shopping arcades were built to meet the needs of the growing numbers of visitors. Fashionable shopping areas developed, such as Oxford Street in the West End. The Burlington Arcade, opened in 1818, was patrolled by Beadles who prohibited whistling, singing or hurrying. Ancient street markets continued to flourish at Portobello, Brixton, Leadenhall and Petticoat Lane. There were other specialised wholesale markets for fruit and vegetables at Covent Garden and Spitalfields, meat at Smithfield and fish at Billingsgate.

The streets of London were a hive of activity swelled by casual and migrant labourers who sought to make a living by street trading. For example, there were 30 000 costermongers dealing in fish, fruit and vegetables. Many of these were illiterate, violent and often the worse for visiting some of the 400 public houses in the city. To keep their trade from both the police and rivals, they developed secret languages and spoke backwards!

Victorian London

The streets were packed with traders and street urchins.

No cars and traffic jams. People used carriages and horses.

The Underground wasn't built until the 1890's

Writing

- Choose a person from the activity sheet and write about a day in their life.
- Write a newspaper report about conditions on the streets of London in the 1860s.

Activities

- The activity should be enlarged to A3 size for the children to write in the speech bubbles.
- They could investigate similar scenes could be found in cities, such as Manchester, Glasgow and Cardiff.
- Extension activities could include investigating why London was such an important city and why many people moved there from the countryside.
- The children could also investigate other jobs in 1860s London, such as chimney sweeps and so on.

Why London was important

* It was the centre of the railway network.
* Its docks handled imports from all over the world.
* Britain's Government was based in London.

London street life

- Write the street cries in the correct speech bubbles.

- Watch the monkey dance!
- Feed the birds! Farthing a bag!
- Crunchy and hot, halfpenny a bag!
- Knives to grind, any knives to grind?
- Halfpenny a box!

- Sweep! sweep!
- Headaches, backaches, miracle cures!
- Lovely violets, roses for your sweetheart!
- Juicy and ripe, who will buy!
- Hot and tasty, freshly baked!

IDEAS BANK – *Victorian Britain*

Key elements

Knowledge and understanding
- To compare and contrast Victorian operating theatres with those today.
- To consider the impact of anaesthetics on surgical operations.

Historical enquiry
- To investigate the development of medical techniques since the Victorian era.

How anaesthetics help

* The patient is asleep.

* The surgeon operates on a still body.

* The patient doesn't feel any pain.

Key questions

- How did operations in Victorian Britain differ from those today?
- How has the use of anaesthetics improved surgical techniques?

Background

The Victorian period was a time of great medical advance. Anaesthetics were discovered and Pasteur produced his 'germ theory' in 1861. Powerful microscopes were developed. Robert Koch's staining techniques in the 1870s led to the development of antiseptics and aseptic (germ-free) surgery.

Before anaesthetics, patients were conscious and in great pain during operations. They had to be held down by their arms and legs and an assistant hit them on the head with a hammer at regular intervals. No lengthy or complicated surgery was possible. Alcohol was used to dull the pain rather than render the patient unconscious.

Experiments with a number of substances were undertaken by doctors and their guests as 'after-dinner games'. Nitrous oxide (laughing gas), often used as a circus act, was tried. Dosages varied and often resulted in death. Hannah Greener, aged 15, was the first person to die under chloroform. Ether was tried and found to be too unstable. The first surgeon in Europe to use anaesthetics was Robert Liston. In one of his operations (a leg amputation), the patient died, as did a surgical assistant whose fingers were cut off. An observer, a senior surgeon, died of shock, making this the only operation in history with a 300% mortality rate!

Some doctors argued that pain was natural and part of the healing process. They believed that pain during childbirth was ordained by God. However, in 1853, chloroform was successfully used on Queen Victoria during childbirth. Afterwards, anaesthetics were widely adopted. However, until the dosage was carefully regulated, unexpected deaths still occurred. Anaesthetics permitted lengthier and more complicated surgery to be attempted. This further increased medical knowledge and understanding of the human body.

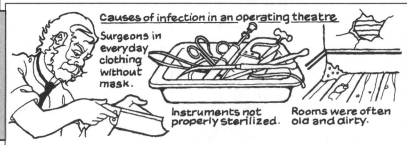

Causes of infection in an operating theatre
Surgeons in everyday clothing without mask.
Instruments not properly sterilized.
Rooms were often old and dirty.

Activities

- The children could investigate and describe the major sources of germs that can cause infection in an operating theatre (such as clothes, chairs, surroundings, visitors, faces not covered with a mask, hands, hair and so on).
- Ask the children to consider the effect of pain-killers on operating techniques. Some children may have their own experiences of operations that they could describe.
- Extension activities could include further investigation about the invention of anaesthetics and antiseptics, and the surgeons who used them, like Robert Liston.

Writing

- Imagine you are a surgeon in a Victorian hospital. Write a letter to one of your patients, explaining what will happen in their operation.
- Write a report of the operation and say what happened.

Medicine

● Look carefully at these two pictures.

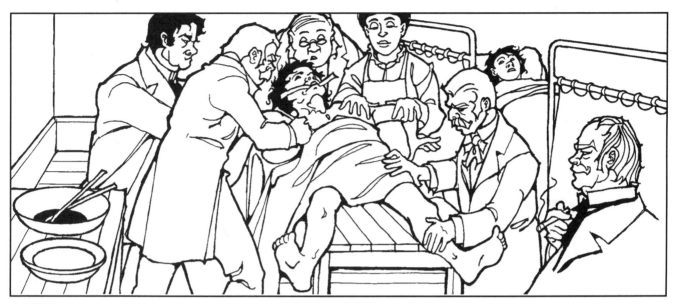

A Victorian operating theatre.

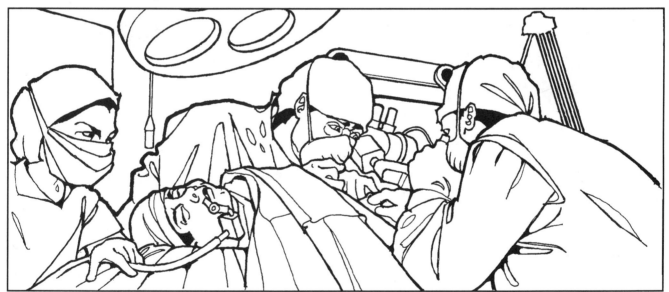

A modern operating theatre.

● Write a list of what is different in these two pictures and
what is the same. Use these words to help you: germs, clean, operation,
surgeon, patient, pain, anaesthetic.
● Why do you think some people died during operations in the
Victorian era?
● Why do you think operations are much safer and less painful today?

      ● Find out more about the invention of anaesthetic
and why it is needed.

The vote –

Key elements

Knowledge and understanding
- To consider the development of the vote.

Chronology
- To sequence the development of the vote within a chronological framework.

Key questions

- When did different groups of people gain the right to vote?
- How quickly was the right to vote extended?

Background

The Great Reform Acts of 1832 gave the vote to all adult males over 21 with property valued at over £100 (this applied to 17% of the total male population.) The Chartists demanded further reforms. Petitions were unsuccessfully presented to Parliament in 1839, 1842 and 1848. Violent protests resulted in deaths occurring in Newport (1839) and Stoke-on-Trent (1842). The Chartist movement declined in the 1850s as a result of internal disagreements and government opposition.

The 1867 Reform Act gave the vote to all men over 21 in towns who owned or rented a house valued at £10 a year. This gave two million men the vote and doubled the voting population.

The 1884 Reform Act gave the same rights to men over 21 in the countryside. Now nearly two-thirds of the adult male population could vote. There were still no plans to extend the franchise to women despite the work of the Suffragettes and other groups. Women attempted to place their names on the register of electors as early as 1868. Not until 1918 were women given the vote.

Writing

- Imagine you are a wealthy woman living in a Victorian town in 1867. Write a letter to the government to explain your views about the vote.
- Imagine that you are a journalist visiting an election scene in 1838. Write a short report describing the scene.

Activities

- Before beginning the activity page, ensure that the children are aware of what the vote is and how elections work. Ask them what they know about elections today.
- The children could discuss the various reasons why people demanded the vote in Victorian Britain. Reasons include increased awareness of politics amongst ordinary people and a desire for representation to gain influence and power.
- Discuss the purpose and value of a time line.
- Role-play: until 1872, before the secret ballot, voters had to climb the 'hustings' and publicly declare their choice of candidate. Mobs for the rival candidates would try to influence the voters by intimidation or bribery. The children could organise an imaginary election campaign at the hustings. This scene will require a returning officer, two candidates, two rival mobs and a group of voters.

Why did voting changes take so long?

1. Rich people wanted all the power.

2. Poor, working classes might have dangerous ideas.

3. Women had other roles to perform in life.

The vote

In the pictures are people who have just been given the vote.
- Read the captions and decide which person got the vote when.
- Write the correct date beneath each picture. One has been done for you.

1867 Skilled male town workers over 21 could vote.	1928 All people over 21 could vote.

1884 Male farm workers over 21 could vote.

1832 Male farmers, factory owners, traders and shopkeepers over 21 could vote.

1918 All women over 30 and men over 21 could vote.

Date: 1867

Date:_____

Date:_____

Date:_____

Date:_____

- Cut out the pictures and put them in the correct order to make a time line.
- Look carefully at your time line. Did changes happen quickly or slowly? Why do you think this was?
- Which of these changes happened after the Victorian era? Why do you think it took so long for them to happen?

- The vote changed again in 1969. Find out what happened and why.

A Victorian prison –  Ideas page

Key elements

Historical inquiry
● To investigate Victorian prisons.
Knowledge and understanding
● To learn about life in a Victorian prison.

Key questions

● What was life like in a Victorian prison?
● Were Victorian prisoners treated fairly?

HAD THEY BEEN INDUSTRIOUS WHEN FREE THEY NEED NOT HAVE DRUDGED HERE LIKE SLAVES

A Victorian prison motto

Background

There were many harsh and cruel punishments for crimes in Victorian Britain. In 1800, nearly 200 crimes carried the death penalty including murder and stealing a rabbit. By 1837, the death penalty was phased out for all crimes except murder and treason. Some prisoners were shipped to penal camps in Australia, but this was stopped in 1853.

Prisons were run by local authorities until 1878. They were often harsh, cruel and dirty places. Prisoners were kept in chains until the 1839 Prisons Act that separated offenders in cells. All prisoners – men, women, children, the old, infirm and the insane – had to do hard labour. Many prisoners were people with debts, but imprisoning debtors was stopped after the author Charles Dickens brought its unfairness to public attention.

Children were gradually separated from older prisoners, although in 1873 there were still 60 boys aged eight to 16 in Springfield Gaol. The aim of these prisons was to punish offenders for their crimes – rehabilitation was not considered. In 1878 all prisons were placed under government control.

Activities

● After labelling the plan, the children could discuss the different areas of the prison and describe what it might have been like to be imprisoned there.
● In groups, the children could research crime and punishment in Victorian Britain and draw up a list of crimes with the punishments associated with them.
● They could also investigate modern-day prisons and compare an aspect of prison life with that in Victorian Britain, such as security, living conditions, sanitation and so on.

Crime	Punishment
Murder	Death
Treason	Death
Stealing	Hard labour in prison
Having debts	Hard labour in prison

A Victorian treadmill

Writing

● Imagine you are imprisoned in Springfield Gaol in 1852. Write a letter home to your family, explaining how you feel and what it is like inside the prison.

A Victorian prison

- Look carefully at the plan of a Victorian prison
- Draw a line from the label to where it is found on the plan.

Where corn was ground into flour

Where prisoners ate their meals

Where prisoners were hung

Where prisoners worked

Where prisoners went for walks

Cells for women prisoners

Cells for prisoners who owed money

Plan of Springfield Prison

Outer wall

Watch tower

Wind mill
Corn mill
Tread wheel

A Ward

B Ward

Dining room

C ward

D Ward

Workshop

Gallows pit

Exercise yard

Debtors' ward

Laundry

Female ward

Infirmary

Stables

Store

Infirmary

Entrance

Where sick prisoners were put

Where prisoners washed clothes

- Using the plan and pictures, answer the following questions:
  1. What stopped the prisoners from escaping?
  2. Which three groups were kept separate? Give reasons for this.
  3. What evidence is there that prisoners worked?

- Imagine you are a prison inspector who has visited Springfield in 1878. Describe the different areas of the prison and the activities of some of the prisoners.

Key elements

Knowledge and understanding
● To identify the distinctive features of a Victorian country house.
● To consider life inside a Victorian country house.

Historical enquiry
● To investigate Victorian style and interior decoration.

Background

'Victorian Gothic' was a popular building style in the mid- to late nineteenth century. This imitated the details of Victorian churches (see the windows in the illustration below). Houses were built to look rich and grand with towers, gables and lots of elaborate ornamentation.

As industries developed and communications improved, the growing middle classes moved to the suburbs where there was more space and cleaner air. There were few building and planning regulations required and so houses of many different sizes and styles were constructed.

Large family houses required a number of servants who could live with the family or in the local area. Some houses had separate entrances for servants and tradesmen, separate back stairs and servants' quarters in the attic or basement.

FOR SALE

Victorian country house

✳ Stunning towers and gables.
✳ Gothic ornamentation.
✳ Extensive servants' quarters.
✳ Full gas lighting.
✳ Roomy stables.

Key questions

● What did a Victorian parlour look like?
● How does this room compare with the rooms in your house?

Activities

● Ask the children to describe a Victorian house as if they were trying to sell it, emphasising the good points.
● Ask them to investigate and then hold a class discussion about how a Victorian country house might be run. Questions could include how many servants were required and what were the heating and lighting arrangements (see page 30).
● The children could also design their own room interior based on Victorian fashions and ideas.
● Extension activities could include finding out about Victorian parlour games, such as charades.

Writing

● Write a description of how the Victorians spent their leisure time at home. Include details about different kinds of people, including poor people, middle-class people and rich people.

Victorian style

● Draw a line between each label and the part of the room it describes.

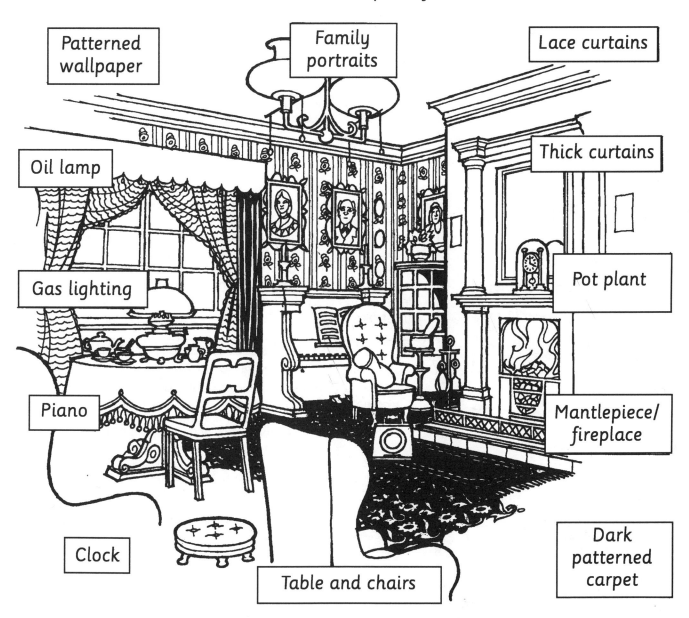

Patterned wallpaper

Family portraits

Lace curtains

Oil lamp

Thick curtains

Gas lighting

Pot plant

Piano

Mantlepiece/ fireplace

Clock

Table and chairs

Dark patterned carpet

● Copy and complete a chart like this to compare a Victorian house with a modern house.

	VICTORIAN HOUSE	MODERN HOUSE
Furniture Ornaments Heating Lighting Home entertainment		

The end of an era –

Key elements

Knowledge and understanding
● To demonstrate factual knowledge of the Victorian era.

Chronology
● To view events of the Victorian era within a chronological framework.

Key questions

● What were the main events of the Victorian Era?

Writing

● Imagine you are an old man or lady who has just witnessed the funeral of Queen Victoria. Write three diary entries from the beginning, middle and end of Victoria's reign. Explain what you were doing at each time and what life was like in Victorian Britain.

● Write a report about what you think was good about the Victorian era and what was bad. What are your conclusions about life in Victorian Britain?

Background

Queen Victoria died in 1901, ending the Victorian era. Her second child, Albert Edward, became King Edward VII. The Edwardian period had begun.

Activities

● Each group of children requires:
  – a board
  – two dice
  – coloured counters.
● The activity page could be enlarged to A3 size to make the game easier to play.
● The teacher reads out one question at a time from the following list. The children put up a hand (or stand up) to show whether they think the answer is true or false. Those giving correct answers should throw the dice and move their piece on the board. (The pictures on the board do not affect play.)

TRUE OR FALSE?

1. Queen Victoria had nine children. **TRUE page 4**
2. Victoria's Golden Jubilee was in 1837. **FALSE (1887) page 4**
3. A diamond Jubilee is 60 years. **TRUE page 4**
4. Steam engines were used to power factories. **TRUE page 6**
5. Natural gas was used at work and at home. **FALSE (coal) page 6**
6. An Overseer kept people working in factories. **TRUE page 8**
7. Weaving machines made coal. **FALSE page 8**
8. A trapper opened and closed doors in a coal mine. **TRUE page 10**
9. A drawer hauled coal in a coal mine. **TRUE page 10**
10. Chicken pox broke out in London in 1862. **FALSE (cholera) page 12**
11. Cholera was spread by drinking dirty water. **TRUE page 12**
12. Cheap wheat was imported from Portugal. **FALSE (Canada/USA) page 14**
13. The Public Health Act was passed in 1838. **FALSE (1848) page 16**
14. Trains were mainly powered by steam. **TRUE page 18**
15. There were five different classes of travel on the railways. **FALSE (three) page 20**
16. The Great Exhibition was in 1852. **TRUE pages 22 and 24**
17. Going to the seaside became popular. **TRUE page 26**
18. The cook was in charge of the servants. **FALSE (butler) page 30**
19. Short skirts were fashionable. **FALSE (long) page 32**
20. Children were not caned at school. **FALSE page 34**
21. Small boys worked as chimney sweeps. **TRUE page 36**
22. Hospitals used pain killers during operations. **FALSE page 38**
23. Everyone over the age of 18 could vote in 1884. **FALSE (men over 21) page 40**
24. Debtors were sent to prison. **TRUE page 42**
25. Many Victorian houses were built in the Gothic style. **TRUE page 44**

The end of an era board game

- You will need two dice and a different coloured counter for each player.
- The winner is the first player to reach the end of the reign in 1901.
- You must answer a question correctly before you roll your dice and move your counter.

1837 Victoria became Queen. START ▶	1838 ▶	1839 Prisons Act. ▶	1840 ▶	1841 ▶	1842 Mines Act. ▼
1848 ▼	1847 ◀	1846 ◀	1845 ◀	1844 Factory Act. ◀	1843 ◀
1849 ▶	1850 ▶	1851 The Great Exhibition. ▶	1852	1853 Victoria is given chloroform during childbirth. ▶	1854 Cholera Epidemic in London. ▼
1860 ▼	1859 ◀	1858 ◀	1857 ◀	1856 ◀	1855 Safety in mines Act. ◀
1861 Prince Albert dies. ▶	1862	1863 ▶	1864 Factory Act. ▶	1865 ▶	1866 ▼
1872 Secret ballot introduced. ▼	1871 ◀	1870 Education Act. ◀	1869 ◀	1868 ◀	1867 Reform Act. ◀
1873 ▶	1874 ▶	1875 Public Health Act. ▶	1876 Victoria becomes Empress of India. ▶	1877 ▶	1878 ▼
1884 Reform Act. ▼	1883 ◀	1882 ◀	1881 ◀	1880 ◀	1879 ◀
1885 ▶	1886 ▶	1887 Golden Jubilee ▶	1888 ▶	1889 ▶	1890 ▼
1896 ▼	1895 ◀	1894 ◀	1893 ◀	1892 ◀	1891 ◀
1897 Diamond Jubilee ▶	1898 ▶	1899 ▶	1900 ▶	1901 Victoria dies. END	

8 ways to help ...

There are many ideas in this book about developing and extending the photocopiable pages. Here are just eight ways to help you make the most of the **Ideas Bank** series.

1
Paste copies of the pages on to card and laminate them. The children could use water-based pens that can be wiped off, allowing the pages to be re-used.

2
Put the pages inside clear plastic wallets. They could be stored in binders for easy reference.
The children's writing can again be easily wiped away.

3
If possible, save the pages for re-use. Develop a simple filing system so that the pages can be easily located for future use.

4
Use both sides of the paper. The children could write or draw on the back of the sheet, or you could photocopy another useful activity on the back.

5
Make the most of group work. Children working in small groups could use one page to discuss between them.

6
Photocopy the pages on to clear film to make overhead transparencies. The ideas can then be used time and time again.

7
Use the activity pages as ideas pages for yourself. Discuss issues and ideas with the class and ask the children to produce artwork and writing.

8
Customise the pages by adding your own activities. Supplement the ideas and apply them to your children's needs.